The
Moon.

A photographic study from a distance of ≈0.002569 astronomical units

The Moon?

I've always been fascinated by the Moon. As a kid I used to stare out of the window a lot at night, but being from the city meant that there was just a meagre spattering of celestial objects in the sky, with the Moon dominating the astronomical landscape. It was the only object I could observe clearly without a telescope, so ended up being the main focus of my attention.

I tried to get my parents to buy me a telescope, but the best I could get out of them was a book called 'The Universe', which I still own. It was full of information I couldn't understand, punctuated by hundreds of amazing illustrations of space. It influenced my desire to leave the planet one day, which in turn influenced my decision to study maths and physics at college, with a view to going on to study astrophysics at university, to become an astronaut, and then to ultimately explore the universe.

Life circumstances put me on a different path, but my fascination with the Moon stuck with me throughout my creative career, so when I started to delve into photography I instinctively pointed my camera at the Moon.

I've taken many many photos of my big, round sky buddy since then but in the last few years I've renewed my interest in astrophotography and taken a lot more, culminating in the collection in this book.

Since the turn of the century we've constantly moved closer to the age of commercial space travel, and every day it looks more likely that my childhood dream of visiting the stars, or at least the Moon, is becoming more realistic.

As you flick through the pages of this book I hope it will inspire you to go out and look at the Moon, think about how vast the universe is, and maybe take some of your own shots.

Temperatures on the Moon have been measured between -250°C and 120°C.

Daytime temperatures near the lunar equator can reach 120°C, hot enough to boil water, whereas a temperature of -250°C has been measured in the floor of the Moon's Hermite Crater, making it the coldest place in the solar system.

The Moon orbits the Earth
once every 27.322 days,
which is a lunar year.
It also rotates on its
own axis once in the same
period of time, which is
a lunar day.

Consequently, a day and a
year on the Moon last
exactly the same amount
of time.

A lunar day and lunar year are exactly the same length of time, lasting 27.322 Earth days.

19

20

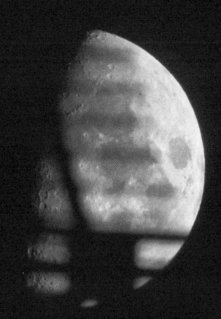

22

The Moon is in synchronous rotation with the Earth, which is why only one side is visible.

The Moon rotates on its
axis at the same speed
as it orbits the Earth,
which means that one side
is permanently facing
us and the other side
(the 'far side') is
permanently facing away.

· ← Saturn

Jupiter → •

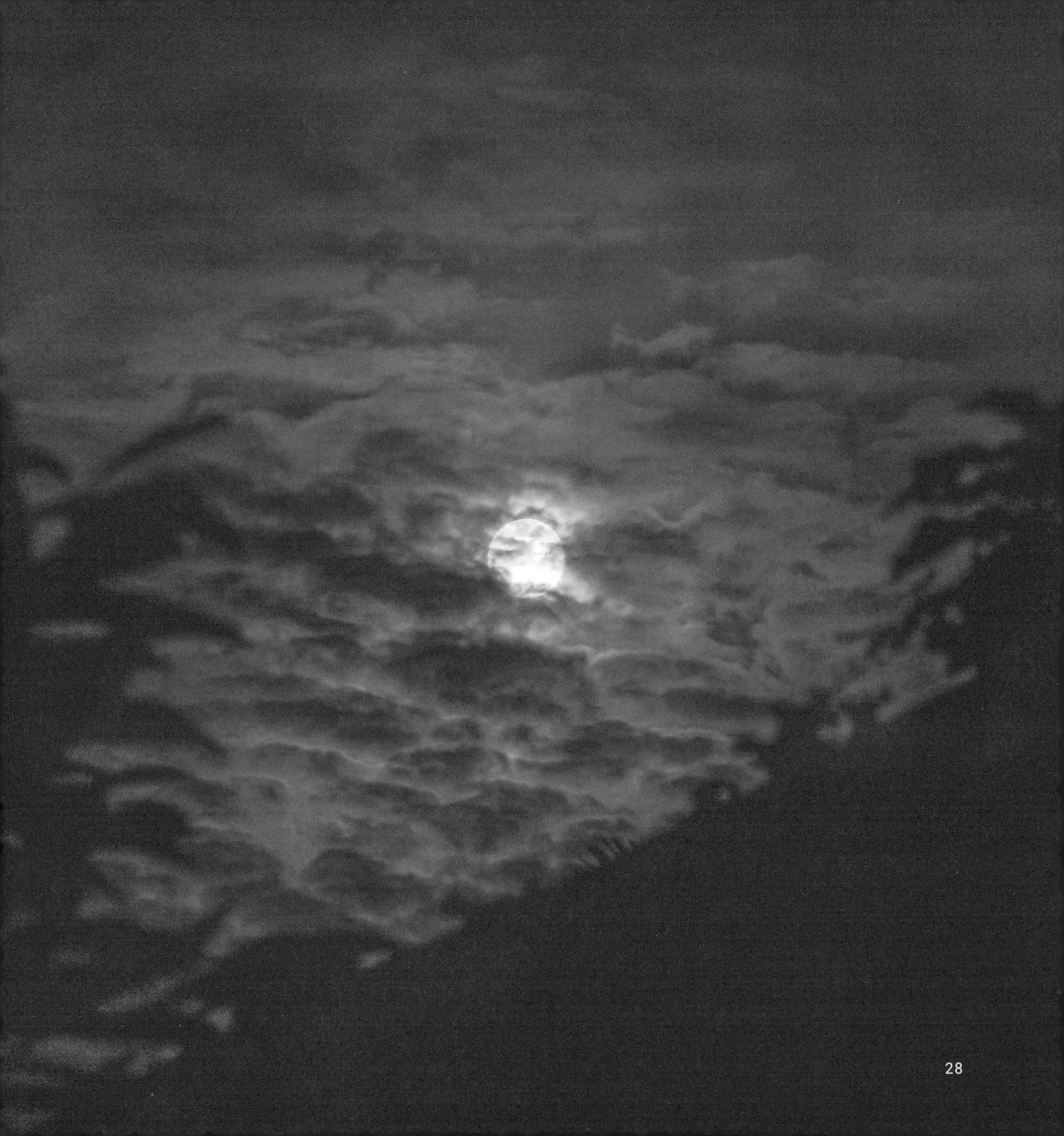

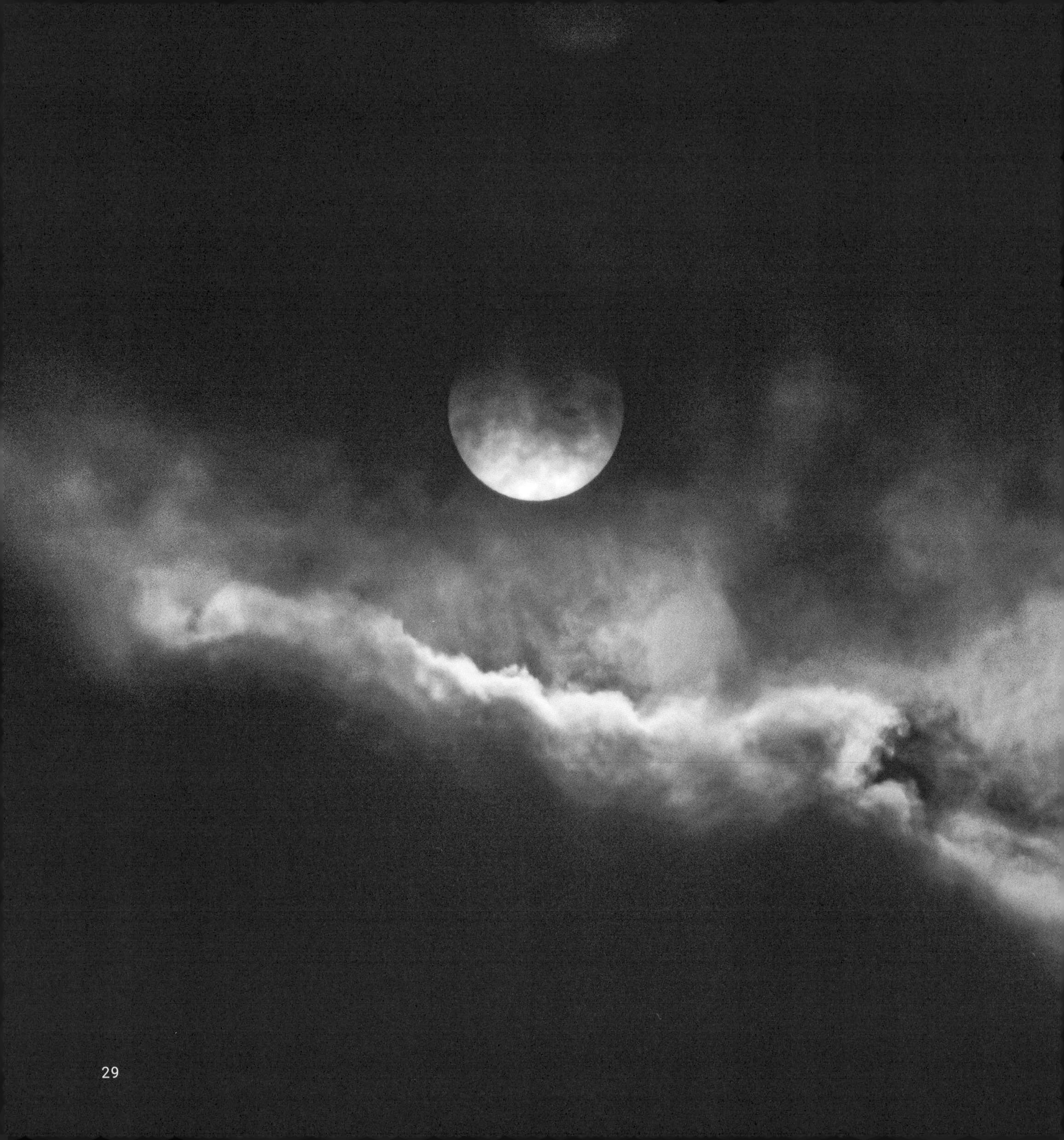

The Moon's diameter is
just under 3,500km,
whereas Australia is
almost 4,000km wide.

The United States in
comparison is 4,500km
wide. The Moon would fit
quite snugly between Las
Vegas and Philadelphia.

The Moon's diameter is comparable to the width of Australia.

33

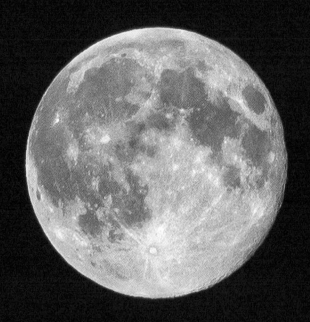

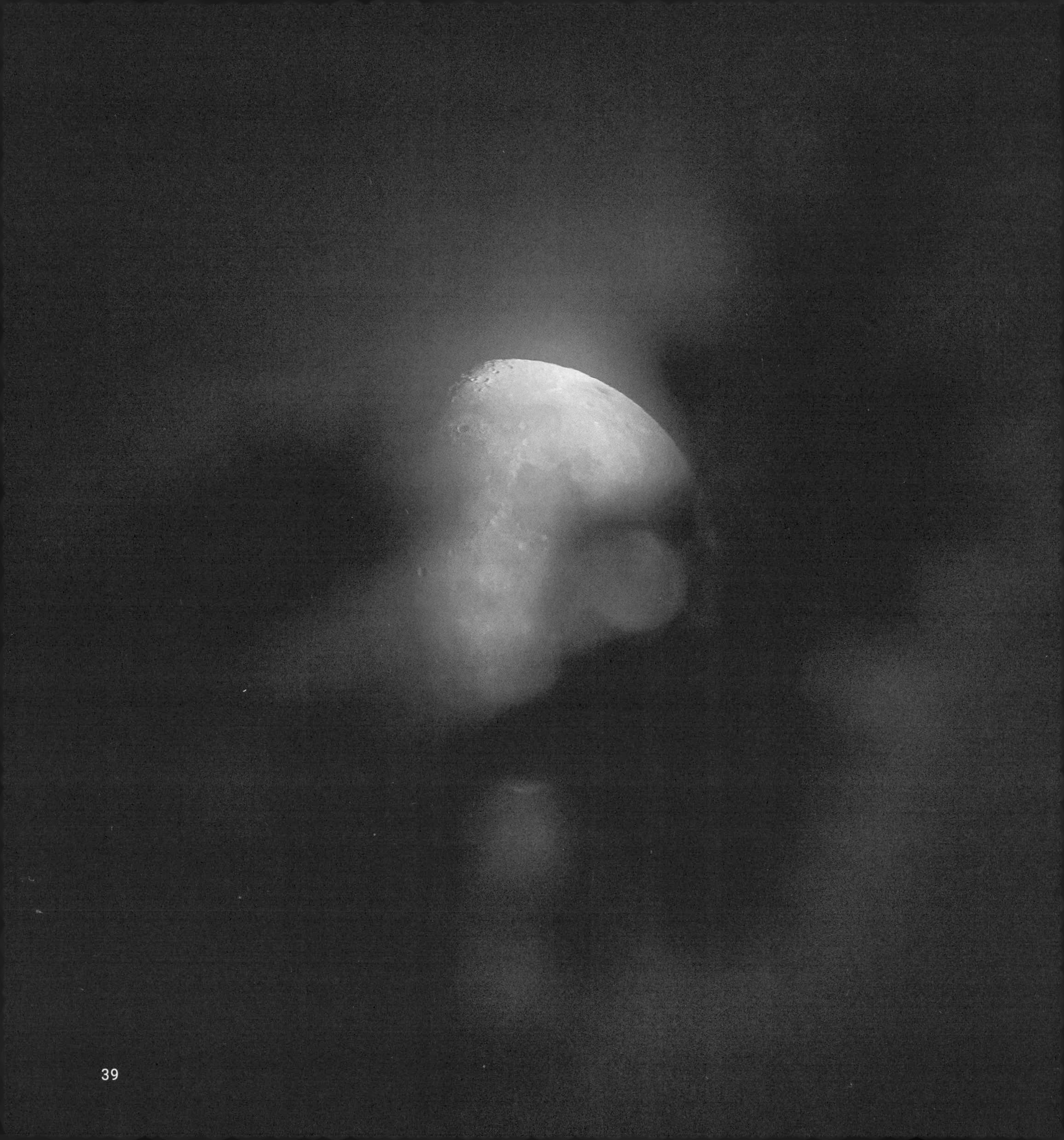

40

The Moon is 400 times smaller and 400 times closer than the Sun, which is why they appear to be the same size in the sky.

This particular
synchonicity of the
universe means that the
Moon and the Sun appear
to be the same size in
the sky. This is what
makes it possible to see
the Sun's corona during
a full lunar eclipse,
rather than the Sun being
completely covered,
or large parts being
visible.

45

Mars → ·

The Moon only appears
bright at night because
of the relative darkness
of your surroundings.
You'll notice that if the
Moon is visible during
the day it can be hard to
even see it.

In fact, the Moon is one
of the least reflective
bodies in the solar
system with a bond albedo
(reflective percentage)
of only 12%, whereas the
Earth has a bond albedo
of 31%, and Venus 75%.

Despite how bright it looks, the Moon's surface is actually only as bright as an asphalt road.

54

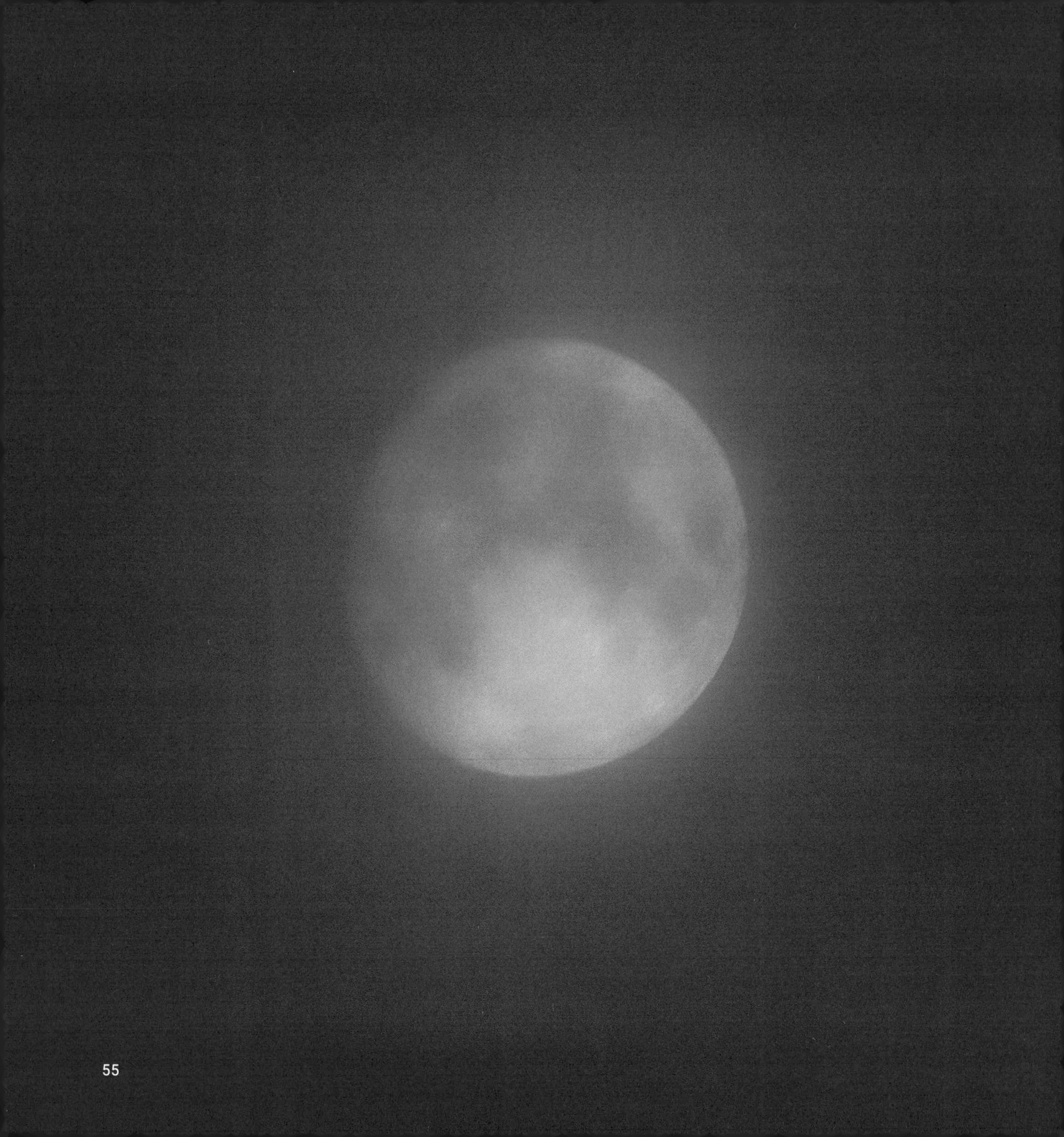

56

Fact→

Every year the Moon moves around 38mm further away from the Earth.

The Moon causes the Earth's tides, but those tides also exert a force on the Moon, making it speed up and move away from the Earth at a rate of 38mm per year, around the same speed that fingernails grow.

61

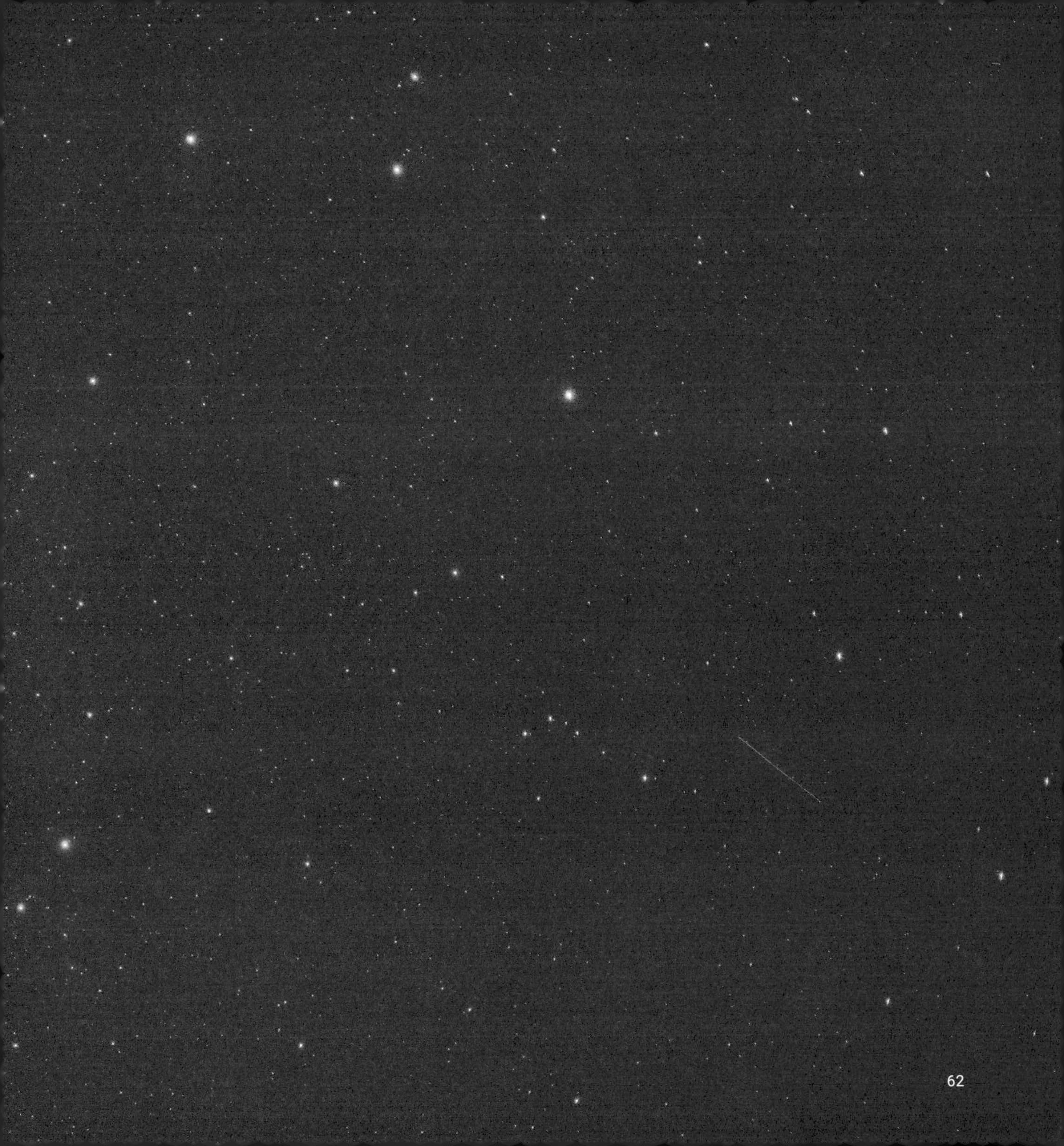

Sound requires particles
to disrupt in order to
cause 'waves' that can
move from one place to
another. The atmosphere
on the Moon is too thin
to carry these waves in
any noticeable manner,
so if you could survive
without a helmet it would
be similar to being in a
vacuum.

That being said, sound
can transmit through the
ground, so if you put
your ears to the surface
you might hear a lunar
quake when one occurs.

The near lack of atmosphere on the Moon means that no sound can travel on the surface, so it's completely silent.

There is no dark side of the Moon. Both sides receive the same amount of sunlight as each other.

It wasn't until 1959
when the Soviet Luna 3
spacecraft took photos of
the far side of the Moon
that humans even knew
what it looked like.

It was a further 9 years
until the Apollo 8
astronauts saw it with
their own eyes in 1968.

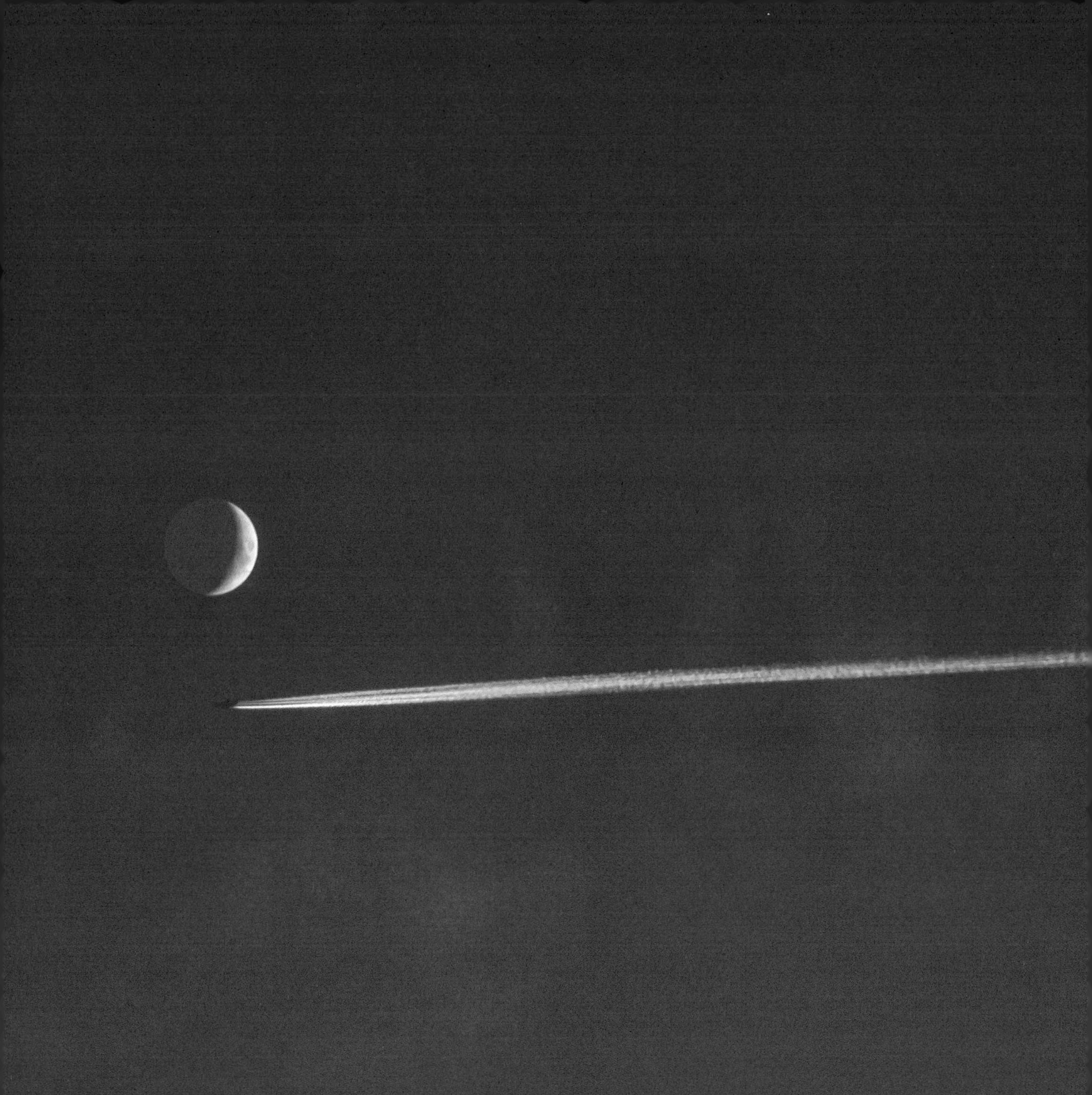

The Moon has consistently been bombarded by asteroids and meteors over its 4.5 billion year life. Because of its lack of atmosphere, tectonics, and volcanic activity, impact craters on the Moon can remain for millions of years. The Earth, by contrast, has around 180 visible impact craters.

There are over 25,000 craters on the Moon that are over 5km in diameter. The lack of weather means that they never erode.